Contents

Counting numbers

Use this number square to help you count to 100.

0	1	2	3	4	5	6	7	8	9
10	11	12	13	14	15	16	17	18	19
20	21	22	23	24	25	26	27	28	29
30	31	32	33	34	35	36	37	38	39
40	41	42	43	44	45	46	47	48	49
50	51	52	53	54	55	56	57	58	59
60	61	62	63	64	65	66	67	68	69
70	71	72	73	74	75	76	77	78	79
80	81	82	83	84	85	86	87	88	89
90	91	92	93	94	95	96	97	98	99

Choose any number and count forwards or backwards from it. Check to see if you know the numbers.

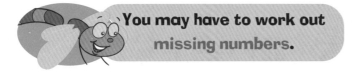

You may have to work out missing numbers.

Just look at the numbers you are given and count on or back.

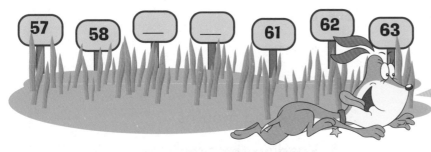

57 58 __ __ 61 62 63

This should be no problem to a clever human like you ... The number after 58 is 59, and then comes 60.

Hutch's workout

1 What number comes after 93? ☐

2 Which number comes between 78 and 80? ☐

3 What are the missing numbers?

47 48 49 ☐ 51 ☐ 53

4 What are the missing numbers?

64 63 ☐ ☐ 60 59 58

A little trickier ...

5 What are the three numbers between 118 and 122? ☐ ☐ ☐

Star points Know your number names.

2

When you count things, make a mark so you don't miss any out.

If there are a lot, try grouping them in 2s, 5s or 10s. You can then count each group.

There are **24** of these pesky Zoids.

Hutch's workout

1 Count each group.

a

b

A little trickier ...

2 Here are 16 lumps of moon-rock.
Draw some more so that there are 25 altogether.

Star points Count carefully.

3

Counting patterns

If you count in different steps you get patterns of multiples.

These are the numbers in the times tables.

Say these numbers out loud and carry the on patterns:

Counting in twos:	2	4	6	8	10 ...
Counting in fives:	5	10	15	20	25 ...
Counting in tens:	10	20	30	40	50 ...
Counting in 100s:	100	200	300	400	500 ...

Look at the patterns of zeros and fives.

Hutch's workout

What are the missing numbers?

1 15 20 ☐ 30 35 ☐ ☐

2 ☐ 8 10 12 ☐ ☐ 18

3 ☐ ☐ 50 60 70 ☐ 90

A little trickier ...

4 20 ☐ 16 ☐ 12 10 ☐

Star points Look at the patterns in multiples.

Number sequences

A sequence of numbers is a list of numbers in a pattern.

To work out the pattern it is best to look at the gap between the numbers.

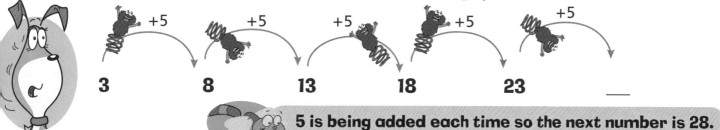

+5   +5   +5   +5   +5

3   8   13   18   23   __

5 is being added each time so the next number is 28.

Here are some more sequences. Can you work out the next number?

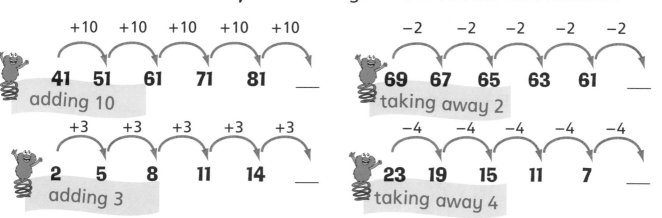

+10   +10   +10   +10   +10

41   51   61   71   81   __

adding 10

−2   −2   −2   −2   −2

69   67   65   63   61   __

taking away 2

+3   +3   +3   +3   +3

2   5   8   11   14   __

adding 3

−4   −4   −4   −4   −4

23   19   15   11   7   __

taking away 4

Hutch's workout

Show the steps and write the next three numbers.

1   13   15   17   19   ☐ ☐ ☐

2   42   37   32   27   ☐ ☐ ☐

3   4   7   10   13   ☐ ☐ ☐

34
21   18

A little trickier ...

4   50   46   42   38   ☐ ☐ ☐

Star points Jump the gap.

Odd and even numbers

These are the odd and even numbers to 20.

Even numbers always end in 0, 2, 4, 6 or 8.

Odd numbers always end in 1, 2, 3, 4 or 9.

Odd

1 3 5 7 9 11 13 15 17 19

Even

2 4 6 8 10 12 14 16 18 20

Even numbers can be divided exactly by 2.

46 72 90 134
Planet Even

73 65 89 107
Planet Odd

Hutch's workout

1 Write the next three numbers.

a   **21   23   25   27**

b   **62   64   66   68**

2 Circle the odd numbers

74   85   93   70   41   67   54

A little trickier ...

3 What are the even numbers between 315 and 321?

Star points The last digit makes a number odd or even.

Place value

There are ten digits used to make all our numbers:

1 2 3 4 5 6 7 8 9 0

The key thing is that these digits can be hundreds, tens or ones.

2-digit numbers have tens and ones:

34 = 30 + 4

1 more: 35 = 30 + 5

75 = 70 + 5

10 more: 85 = 80 + 5

3-digit numbers have hundreds, tens and ones:

138 = 100 + 30 + 8

1 more: 139 = 100 + 30 + 9

217 = 200 + 10 + 7

10 more: 227 = 200 + 20 + 7

Hutch's workout

1 What does the 3 in 38 stand for?

2 What does the 6 stand for in 684?

3 Complete this sum:

157 = 100 + ☐ + ☐

4 What is one more than 78?

5 What is ten more than 135?

A little trickier ...

6 What is the next number after 499?

Star points Look at the position of the digits.

Reading and writing numbers

You can write numbers in words or with digits.

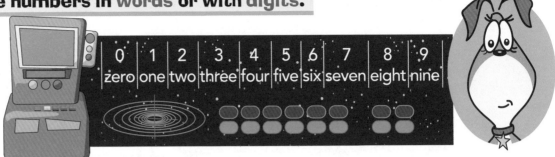

0	1	2	3	4	5	6	7	8	9
zero	one	two	three	four	five	six	seven	eight	nine

Be careful with the 'teen' numbers. We say them differently to other numbers:

11 eleven   12 twelve   13 thirteen   14 fourteen   15 fifteen

16 sixteen   17 seventeen   18 eighteen   19 nineteen

Two-digit numbers

Write the **tens** then the **ones**:

37 → thirty-seven

54 → fifty-four

Three-digit numbers

Write the **hundreds** then the **tens** then the **ones**:

142 → one hundred and forty-two

698 → six hundred and ninety-eight

Do you notice that it is hundred, not hundreds?

Hutch's workout

1 Write these as digits:

a ninety-four →

b eighty-seven →

c one hundred and fifty-one →

2 Write these as words:

a 63 →

b 75 →

c 242 →

A little trickier ...

3 Write 509 in words →

Star points
Say the **hundreds**: six hundred
Then the **tens**:   and ninety-
Then the **ones**:   eight

Comparing

When you need to find out which number is bigger or smaller you compare the digits.

Which number is bigger 54 or 45?

54 is the same as 50 + 4

45 is the same as 40 + 5

Look at the tens. **54** is bigger than **45**.

Number lines are great for comparing numbers.
Just remember that numbers are **bigger** as you move to the **right**.

> Bigger doesn't mean a bigger size, it means a greater or higher number!

24 is bigger than 17 because it's further to the right.

Hutch's workout

1 Which is greater, 78 or 84?

2 Which is smaller, 64 or 59?

3 Which is the bigger number, 123 or 321?

4 Which is the smaller number, 406 or 178?

A little trickier ...

5 Tick the smallest number and put a cross on the biggest.

93   102   87   90   179   210

Star points Compare the digits: hundreds, tens and ones.

Ordering

If you're given a list of numbers to put in order, look at the tens first and then at the ones.

Put these in order starting with the smallest.

Check the tens: 43   59   68   65   71

Check the ones: **65** is smaller than **68**

Put in order: 43   59   65   68   71

Use a 100-square or a number line to help you put numbers in order.

Hutch's workout

1 Put these numbers in order, starting with the largest.

56   81   37   59   78   85

2 Put these amounts in order, starting with the smallest.

18p   65p   13p   8p   82p   60p

3 Join these numbers to the correct place on the number line.

57   49   42   51   46   54

```
40                        50                        60
```

little trickier ...

4 Put these numbers in order, starting with the largest.

124   101   94   129   115   99

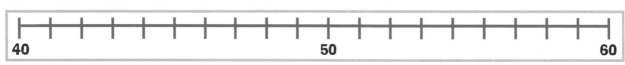

Star points Order the tens then the ones.

Estimating

Are you a good estimator?

Have a quick look at this pile of zoids.
Do you think there are **more** or **less** than 20?
How many do you think there are?

Count the zoids to see how good your estimate was.

Estimating is a bit like guessing, but it shouldn't just be a wild guess. If you are good with numbers try to **roughly count them in groups of 5 or 10.** You don't need to be exact, an **approximate** answer is all you need.

You may need to estimate the position of a point on a line.

Just find the half-way position and count on or back to work it out.

Hutch's workout

1 Approximately how many bottles of astro-pop are there?

2 Estimate the number of star sweets.

A little trickier ...

3 Which numbers are the arrows pointing to?

10   ↑   ↑   ↑   30

Star points Quickly count in groups of ten ... then estimate.

Rounding

A 'round number' is a number ending in zero.

0   10   20   30   40   50   60   70   80   90   100

Rounding a number means finding the nearest 10.

For any number, look at the '**ones**' digit.

- If it is **5 or more**, **round up** to the next ten.

- If it is **less than 5**, **round down** to the ten before.

34 rounds down to 30

57 rounds up to 60

45 rounds up to 50

A number is always between two 'round' numbers, you just have to choose which one it's nearest to. Use the number line to help you.

Hutch's workout

1 Round these numbers to the nearest ten.

a 36 =

c 85 =

b 74 =

d 63 =

A little trickier ...

2 What is 125 rounded to the nearest ten?

Star points
5 or more round up.
Less than 5 round down.

Fractions

All you need to think about are halves and quarters.

Halving is making something into **two equal bits**.

It could be a pizza…    … or a piece of paper.

It could be eight grapes …   … or six ice creams.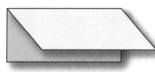

$\frac{1}{2}$ of 8 is 4 $\frac{1}{2}$ of 6 is 3

 $\frac{1}{2}$ is one-half and $\frac{1}{4}$ is one-quarter.

If there are 4 equal parts, it is in **quarters**.

 Look at the cake. Can you see that two quarters is the same as one-half?

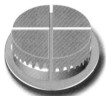 $\frac{1}{4}$ of 8 is 2

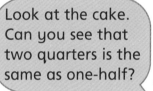

Hutch's workout

1 Colour half of this flag red.

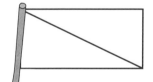

2 What fraction of this square is blue?

3 Draw a circle around $\frac{1}{4}$ of these zoids.

4 What is $\frac{1}{2}$ of 14?

A little trickier …

5 Dan makes 16 pancakes. When he tosses them, $\frac{1}{4}$ are stuck to the ceiling so he can't eat them. How many does he eat?

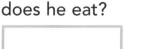 Splatt!

Star points
$\frac{1}{2}$ means two equal parts.
$\frac{1}{4}$ means four equal parts.

Try to be really quick at adding numbers to 20.

Use this grid to help.

What is 5 + 7?

Read across from 5 and down from 7. Where they meet is the answer: **12**.

1	2	3	4	5	6	7	8	9	10
2	4	5	6	7	8	9	10	11	12
3	5	6	7	8	9	10	11	12	13
4	6	7	8	9	10	11	12	13	14
5	7	8	9	10	11	(12)	13	14	15
6	8	9	10	11	12	13	14	15	16
7	9	10	11	12	13	14	15	16	17
8	10	11	12	13	14	15	16	17	18
9	11	12	13	14	15	16	17	18	19
10	12	13	14	15	16	17	18	19	20

Remember that 5 + 7 has the same answer as 7 + 5. It doesn't matter which number you start with.

Colour in the facts on the grid that you know quickly.

Practice the ones you don't know.

Hutch's workout

1 Answer these as quickly as you can.

a 4 + 7 = ☐

b 3 + 9 = ☐

c 6 + 8 = ☐

d 5 + 4 = ☐

e 9 + 2 = ☐

A little trickier ...

2 Write the missing numbers to complete the trail.

 3 + ☆ → 8 + ☆ → 12 + ☆ → 15 + ☆ → 20

Star points Total numbers to ten as quickly as you can.

Using doubles

Try to learn these doubles

1 + 1 = 2	2 + 2 = 4	3 + 3 = 6	4 + 4 = 8	5 + 5 = 10
6 + 6 = 12	7 + 7 = 14	8 + 8 = 16	9 + 9 = 18	10 + 10 = 20

If you know these, then you can quickly work out **near-doubles**.

Double 6 is 12
6 + 7 is 1 more
= 13

Double 5 is 10
5 + 4 is 1 less
= 9

Double 7 is 14
8 + 7 is 1 more
= 15

Double 9 is 18
9 + 8 is 1 less
= 17

You can use doubles with **bigger numbers**.

Double 40 is 80
40 + 41
= 81

Double 30 is 60
30 + 29
= 59

Double 50 is 100
50 + 51
= 101

Double 80 is 160
80 + 79
= 159

Hutch's workout

1 a 8 + 8 =   b 8 + 9 =

2 a 10 + 10 =   b 10 + 11 =

3 5 + 6 =

4 7 + 8 =

A little trickier ...

5 70 + 69 =

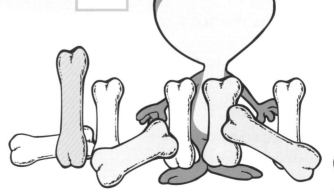

Star points If the sum is near to a double ... use it.

Adding

Adding bigger numbers in your head is OK if you break the numbers up.

How many bones are there altogether?

1 Hold the biggest number in your head.
35

2 Break up the smaller number into tens and ones.
24 → 20 and 4

3 Add the tens.
35 + 20 = 55

4 Add the ones.
55 + 4 = 59

When you add 29, add 30 and take away 1.
52 + 29 → 52 add 30 is 82, take away 1 is 81.

When you add 39, add 40 and take away 1.
47 + 39 → 47, add 40 is 87, take away 1 is 86.

You can do this to add, 49, 59, 69, 79 …

Hutch's workout

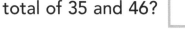

1 52 + 34 =

2 What is the total of 35 and 46?

3 How much is 43p and 48p altogether?

4 Add together 59 and 37.

A little trickier …

5 What is 68 added to 99?

Star points Break up the numbers to add.

Taking away

When you take away the number gets smaller.

Here are 8 lettuces. If 3 are eaten, how many are left?

8 − 3 = 5

What is 11 take away 4? ☐

Try counting back to find the answer.

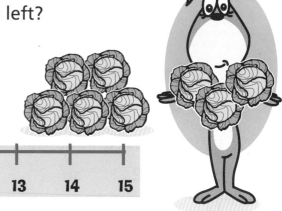

| | | | | | | | | | | |
|5|6|7|8|9|10|11|12|13|14|15|

11 − 4 = 7

This works well if you need to take a small number from a big numbers.

What is 3 less than 62? ☐

Count back from 62.

| | | | | | | | |
|57|58|59|60|61|62|63|64|

62 − 3 = 59

Hutch's workout

1 13 − 5 = ☐

2 What is 18 take away 6? ☐

3 What is 4 less than 31? ☐

4 52 − 5 = ☐

A little trickier ...

5 What is this showing?

| | | | | | | | | | | |
|75|76|77|78|79|80|81|82|83|84|85|

☐ − ☐ = ☐

Star points Count back to take away.

These are a set of trios.

These three numbers can be put together to make these trio sums.

4 + 5 = 9   5 + 4 = 9   9 − 4 = 5   9 − 5 = 4

So if you know an addition, you can work out a subtraction.

8 + 4 = 12   so ...

12 − 4 = 8   and   **12 − 8 = 4**

This is useful for missing number problems. Use the numbers you are given to work out the number in the box.

[   ] **− 5 = 6**

5 add 6 is 11, so 11 is the missing number:

11 − 5 = 6

13 − [   ] **= 9**

13 take away 9 is 4, so 4 is the missing number:

13 − 4 = 9

Hutch's workout

1 7 + [   ] = 10

2 14 − [   ] = 8

3 [   ] + 9 = 15

4 [   ] − 6 = 6

A little trickier ...

5 What facts can be made from 8, 7 and 15?

[   ]   [   ]

[   ]   [   ]

Star points A trio can make four facts:

7   11
4

7 + 4 = 11   11 − 7 = 4
4 + 7 = 11   11 − 4 = 7

Differences

What is the difference between 8 and 14?

Don't be confused by the word 'difference'. Here it means 'how many more is 14 than 8' so you're trying to work out the gap between 8 and 14.

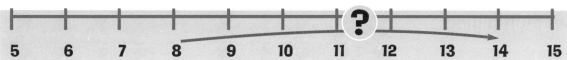

Try counting on from 8 to 10 and then on to 14.

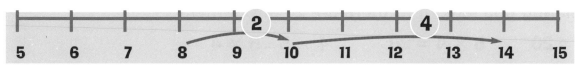

So the difference between 8 and 14 is 6.

Counting on works well with big numbers.

52 – 47 = ☐

This is the same as 14-8, so if you have a question like this you can count on to find the difference.

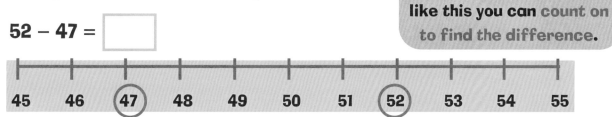

Count on from 47 to 50 (hold the 3 in your head). Count on from 50 to 52 (2).

2 added to 3 is 5 → **52 – 47 = 5**

Hutch's workout

1 What is the difference between 16 and 9? ☐

2 What is the difference between 33 and 26? ☐

3 41 – 35 = ☐   **4** 52 – 29 = ☐

A little trickier ...

5 Which two numbers have a difference of 8?

24   18   21   28   32   ☐ ☐

Star points Count on to find the difference.

Multiplying

If you count things in groups you are multiplying.

The sign we use is ×.

This group of line-dancing zoids shows multiplying beautifully.

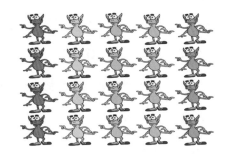

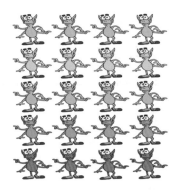

Whichever way you look at it, there are 20 altogether.

$4 × 5 = 20$ $\qquad$ $5 × 4 = 20$ $\qquad$ $4 × 5 = 5 × 4$

A multiplication can be written both ways round and the answer is the same.

$3 × 4 = 4 × 3$ $\qquad$ $8 × 2 = 2 × 8$ $\qquad$ $5 × 6 = 6 × 5$ $\qquad$ $10 × 4 = 4 × 10$

12 $\qquad\qquad$ 16 $\qquad\qquad$ 30 $\qquad\qquad$ 40

Hutch's workout

1 What is 5 multiplied by 3?

2 You can buy stamps in books of 10. How many stamps are in 6 books?

3 $8 × 3 =$

4 There are 4 lilypads on a pond. Each lilypad has 4 frogs sitting on it. How many frogs are there altogether?

A little trickier ...

5 Look at the tins of dog food and complete these sums.

$3 ×$ ☐ $=$ ☐ $\qquad$ $6 ×$ ☐ $=$ ☐

Star points Multiplying is the same both ways round $3 × 10 = 10 × 3$.

20

Dividing

Dividing is the opposite of multiplying

You can divide by **sharing** or putting things in **groups**.

12 carrots shared between 3.
Each person has 4 carrots.

12 ÷ 3 = 4

12 carrots grouped into 3s.
There are 4 groups of 3

12 ÷ 4 = 3

Try counting in groups to work out a division.

What is 30 divided by 5? ☐

Don't worry if something can't divide exactly, just leave some left over as a remainder.

Say this as 'How many 5s make 30?'
6 lots of 5 make 30,
so **30 ÷ 5 = 6**

This is important – use multiplication to help work out division.

How many 2s make 14?

7 twos are 14.

14 ÷ 2 = ☐

7 × 2 = 14

14 ÷ 2 = 7

So 14 divided by 2 is 7.

Hutch's workout

1 What is 18 divided by 3? ☐

3 15 ÷ 5 = ☐

2 How many £2 coins do you get for £20? ☐

4 What is 20 divided by 4? ☐

A little trickier ...

5 10 tennis balls are put into tubes. Each tube holds 3 tennis balls. How many tubes are filled? ☐

Star points Divide by grouping

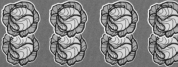

8 ÷ 2 = 4.

Try to learn the 2 and 3 times table so you can say them off by heart.

The numbers in the **2 times tables** are all even. It is the same as **doubling** a number.

Counting in threes is OK, but to learn these **use facts you already know.**

For example 5 × 3 is 15, so 6 × 3 is just 3 more. 10 × 3 is 30, so 9 × 3 is 3 less.

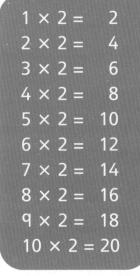

1 × 2 =	2
2 × 2 =	4
3 × 2 =	6
4 × 2 =	8
5 × 2 =	10
6 × 2 =	12
7 × 2 =	14
8 × 2 =	16
9 × 2 =	18
10 × 2 =	20

1 × 3 =	3
2 × 3 =	6
3 × 3 =	9
4 × 3 =	12
5 × 3 =	15
6 × 3 =	18
7 × 3 =	21
8 × 3 =	24
9 × 3 =	27
10 × 3 =	30

They are easy to learn when they are written in order like this – but try to remember them so that you don't need to say them in order.

Write down any that you are not sure of and try to learn them.

Hutch's workout

Remember, 3 X 4 is the same as 4 X 3, it doesn't matter which way round it's written.

1 Answer these as quickly as you can.

a	4 x 3		c	2 x 5		e	2 x 3		g	4 x 2		i	3 x 3	
b	2 x 2		d	10 x 3		f	3 x 5		h	2 x 10		j	1 x 3	

A little trickier ...

2 Answer these as quickly as you can.

a	6 x 3		c	2 x 8		e	7 x 2		g	8 x 3	
b	3 x 9		d	7 x 3		f	2 x 6		h	9 x 2	

Star points Use facts you know to help learn others.

5 and 10 times tables

You need to be able to say the 5 and 10 times table as quickly as you can.

Look at the **patterns** and you can see that this is really easy.

Numbers in the 5x table always end in **5** or **0**.

1 × 5 =	5
2 × 5 =	10
3 × 5 =	15
4 × 5 =	20
5 × 5 =	25
6 × 5 =	30
7 × 5 =	35
8 × 5 =	40
9 × 5 =	45
10 × 5 =	50

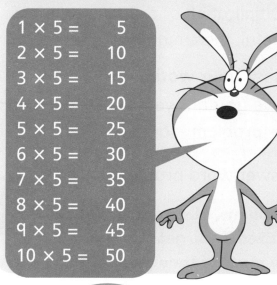

Numbers in the 10x table always end in **0**.

1 × 10 =	10
2 × 10 =	20
3 × 10 =	30
4 × 10 =	40
5 × 10 =	50
6 × 10 =	60
7 × 10 =	70
8 × 10 =	80
9 × 10 =	90
10 × 10 =	100

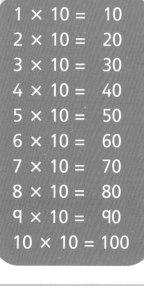

When it is 5 times an odd number the answer ends in 5 and when it is 5 times an even number the answer ends in 0.

Hutch's workout

1 Answer these as quickly as you can.

a **5 x 3**   c **1 x 10**   e **5 x 5**   g **4 x 10**   i **10 x 3**

b **2 x 5**   d **10 x 10**   f **10 x 5**   h **5 x 4**   j **2 x 10**

A little trickier ...

2 Answer these as quickly as you can.

a **6 x 5**   c **10 x 8**   e **7 x 5**   g **8 x 5**

b **10 x 9**   d **7 x 10**   f **10 x 6**   h **9 x 5**

Star points Look at the patterns to help you learn your tables.

23

Maths word problems are just disguised sums, so read them carefully and take your time.

1 Read the problem.
What do you need to find out?
Try to 'picture' the problem and imagine it in real life.

2 Sort out the calculations.
Is it an addition, subtraction, multiplication or division … and be careful, there may be more than one.

3 Work out the answer.
Which mental or written methods will you use?

4 Check your work.
Have you answered all the parts to the problem – read it again.

You may need one or more calculations to answer word problems.

When you answer maths problems, always show your working out on the page. Even if you get the final answer wrong you may have parts of it correct. With a bit of luck you may even be given an extra mark!

Hutch's workout

1 Chris throws a double 6 and a 10 with two darts. What is his total score?

2 In her swimming lesson, Jo swam 20 m, then 25 m and then 40 m. How far did she swim altogether?

3 A coach carries 60 people. How many people will two coaches carry?

4 A book has 32 pages. Sam reads 11 pages on one day and 8 the next day. How many more pages has he got left to read?

A little trickier …

5 A pet shop has 19 rabbits and 8 guinea pigs. They are put together and divided into 3 large pens. How many pets are in each pen?

Star points Picture the problem.

24

Money

Make sure you know all the coins and their value.

100p = £1

From this you can work out how many of each coin makes £1.

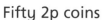

Fifty 2p coins

Twenty 5p coins

Ten 10p coins

Five 20p coins

Two 50p coins

£1.35 = 135p

The point separates the pounds from the pence. So this is £1 and 35 pence. You don't need to write the p, just the £

When you are finding totals of a set of coins, always start with the **highest value coins first**. Then you can add the smallest coins.

Find the total:

£1+50p+20p+5p+2p+1p
= £1.78

Hutch's workout

1 How much is this?

2 160 p = £ _____

3 £2.45 = _____ p

4 Four coins were given to pay the exact price for a drink costing 36p. Which coins were they?

A little trickier ...

5 A bucket costs £3 more than a spade. A spade costs £1.50. How much does it cost for both a bucket and a spade?

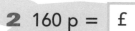

Star points
There are 100 pence in £1

£3.85 → £3 and 85p → 385p.

Giving change

If a comic costs 85p and you give a £1 coin, you will hope to get some change.

To work this out, use coins to **count on** from the price of the comic up to £1.

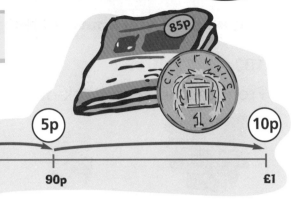

85p up to 90p is 5p.

90p up to £1 is 10p.

So the change given is 5p + 10p, which is 15p.

**This newspaper costs 37p.
What change will there be from 50p?**

37p up to 38p is 1p.

38p up to 40p is 2p.

40p up to 50p is 10p.

So the change given is 1p + 2p + 10p, which is 13p.

Hutch's workout

1 A cake costs 29p. What change will there be from 50p?

2 What is the change from £1 for a sandwich costing 78p?

3 A drink costs 58p. What change is given from £1?

4 Laura bought three plums at 15p each.
How much change from £1 did she get?

A little trickier ...

5 Joe buys a book and gives a £2 coin. He is given 6p change.
How much was the book?

Star points Count on to work out the change.

Sorting diagrams

Venn and Carroll diagrams are very useful for sorting things out.

You could use them to sort out the triangles.

Venn diagram

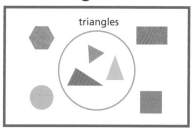

Carroll diagram

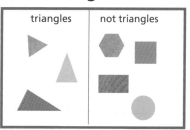

These diagrams sort out numbers.

Compare them and look carefully at each part.

	even numbers	not even numbers
greater than 10	14 18 16	17 15
not greater than 10	8	1 9 5 7

• This shows the set of even numbers not greater than 10.

• This shows the set of numbers greater than 10 and not even.

• This shows even numbers that are greater than 10.

• This shows numbers that are not even or greater than 10.

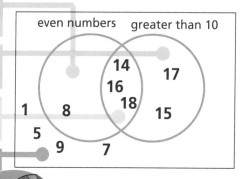

Hutch's workout

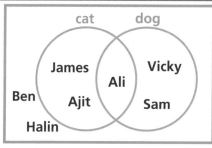

1 Who has a cat but no dog?

2 Who has a cat and a dog?

3 Who has a dog but no cat?

4 Who has no cat or dog?

A little trickier ...

5 Draw a Carroll diagram so that it shows the same information as this Venn diagram.

Star points
Sort onto different parts of a Venn or Carrol diagram.

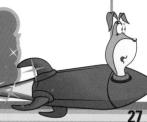

Pictograms are a fun way of showing information.

They use **pictures** to show a number of items.

This pictogram shows the favourite flavour soups of a group of space travellers.

 5 cans show that 10 people chose chicken soup as their favourite.

mushroom	
tomato	
chicken	
vegetable	

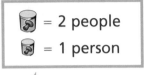

🥫 = 2 people

🥫 = 1 person

6 and a half cans shows that 13 people chose vegetable soup as their favourite.

Check the key. Make sure you know exactly what each single picture is showing. Each picture of a can of soup stands for 2 people.

Hutch's workout

🪐 = 5 planets   🪐🌗 = between 5 and 10 planets

Roy's Rocket	
Galaxy Bus	
Star Tours	
Space Hopper	
Sun Traveller	

1 How many planets are visited by Star Tours?

2 Which space-craft visits 15 planets?

3 How many planets are visited by the Galaxy Bus?

4 Which space-craft visits 12 planets?

A little trickier ...

5 Space Hopper visits three fewer planets than Star Tours. How many planets does Space Hopper visit?

Star points Check the value of each picture.

Bar charts

We use bar charts to show information because they are so clear and simple: **each bar shows an amount.**

Don't make silly mistakes though, you need to read all the parts of the graph carefully before you begin.

This graph shows the number of yo-yos sold from a yo-yo shop. Sales were a bit up and down during the week!

Look at the axis labels - these explain the lines that go up and across.

Work out the scale - look carefully at the numbers, this goes up in twos.

Read the title - work out what it is all about.

Compare the bars - read them across to work out the amounts.

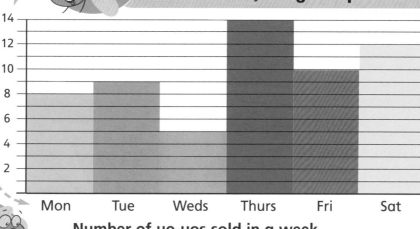

Number of yo-yos sold in a week

Look at each day – which day had the most sales? Which day had the fewest?

Hutch's workout

This graph shows the favourite activities of some very lazy people.

1 Which activity was chosen the most?

2 How many people chose watching television?

3 Which activity did nine people choose?

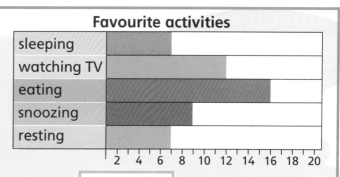

Favourite activities

A little trickier ...

4 How many more people chose eating than snoozing?

Star points Read each part of a graph.

Length

We use a ruler or tape measure to find the length of objects.

| 0 | 1 | 2 | 3 | 4 | 5 | 6 | 7 | 8 | 9 | 10 | 11 | 12 | 13 | 14 | 15 |

Length is measured using **centimetres** and **metres**.

1 metre (m) = 100 cm

When you use a ruler, line up one end with zero. This caterpillar is 9 cm long.

Before you measure something it is a good idea to work out roughly how long it is. This is called estimating. Use these lines to help you estimate.

| 1 cm | 5 cm | 10 cm |

Your hand-span is about 10 cm long, so this can also help you estimate.

Hutch's workout

1 What is the length of this snake?

2 1 m 50 cm = ☐ cm

3 My cat is 35 cm tall. My dog is 45 cm taller. How tall is my dog? ☐

4 Is your shoe longer or shorter than 10 cm? ☐
What is the exact length of one of your shoes?

A little trickier …

5 Estimate the height of a door. Measure to check your estimate. ☐

Star points Estimate then measure using centimetres or metres.

Mass

We measure **mass** or **weight** (they mean just about the same thing) using **grams** and **kilograms**.

1 kilogram (kg) = 1000 grams (g)

One gram is a tiny amount and kilograms can get very heavy. To help you **estimate** mass, learn these **approximate** amounts:

1 gram = a pinch of salt

20 grams = a spoonful of sugar

100 grams = a small apple

1000 grams or 1 kilograms = a bag of sugar.

Try to get a feel for these by holding different objects and 'weighing' them in your hands. Then you can start comparing.

Hutch's workout

1 What is the weight of these mushrooms?

2 2 kg 500 g = ☐ g

3 Approximately how heavy is a pencil, 20 g or 200 g? ☐

4 There are 5 kg of oranges in one box. How many kilograms of oranges are in four boxes? ☐

A little trickier ...

5 Estimate the weight of a shoe. ☐ Measure to check your estimate.

Star points
Know your number names.

1 zoid weighs 10 kg.

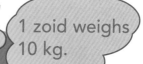

Capacity

We measure liquids using millilitres and litres.

1 litre (l) = 1000 millilitres (ml)

Most cups hold about 300 ml, so 1 millilitre is a tiny drop of water. Bottles of drink are usually 1 or 2 litres.

It is a good idea to get to know how much 100 ml is, then you can compare amounts. Try this activity (and don't get too wet!).

• Fill a jug up to 100 ml and pour it into a 1 litre plastic bottle.

• Put an elastic band around the bottle to mark the level.

• Pour in another 100 ml and mark it with another elastic band.

• Keep doing this until you have the bottle marked to the top.

Find different cups and containers and estimate how many millilitres they hold. Then check with your bottle.

950 ml

Whenever you measure with a jug you need to look carefully at the labelled marks that show the amount. Read them to the nearest line.

Hutch's workout

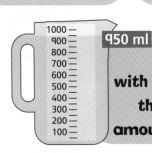

1 How much liquid is in this jug?

2 1l 200 ml = [ ] ml

3 If you have 60 litres of water, how many 10 litre buckets can you fill? [ ]

A little trickier ...

4 A jug holds 900 ml of water. Approximately how many cupfuls will this fill? Measure to check. [ ]

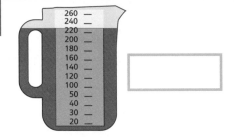

Star points Estimate then measure using millilitres or litres.

Days and months

Check that you know all these time facts.

1 minute = 60 seconds   **1 hour = 60 minutes**   **1 day = 24 hours**

There are **7 days in a week**. Try to learn the order:

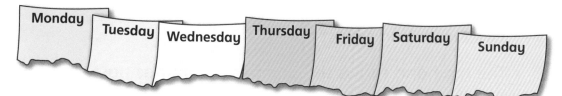

Monday   Tuesday   Wednesday   Thursday   Friday   Saturday   Sunday

There are **12 months in a year**, which is 365 days.

A leap year has 366 days. This happens every four years.

Learn the order:

January	April	July	October
February	May	August	November
March	June	September	December

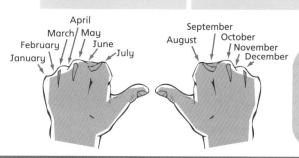

April
March / May
February / June / July
January

September
August / October
November
December

Use your knuckles to learn the days of the months. All the 'knuckle months' have 31 days. February has 28 days (29 days in a leap year) and April, June, September and November have 30 days.

Hutch's workout

1 Which day comes before Thursday?

2 How many hours are in a day?

3 Which month comes after October?

4 How many days in May?

A little trickier ...

5 Calculate the number of months, weeks and days to your birthday.

Star points Learn the order of days and months.

Reading the time

To read the time you need to make sense of the little hour hand and the big minute hand

- The little hand is the **hour hand**. It shows each hour from 1 to 12. This is pointing to just past the 8.

- The big hand shows the number of **minutes** past the hour. You need to count round in 5s. This is pointing to 15.

> The time is 8.15, which is 15 minutes past 8. We also say a quarter-past eight.

This is how to read the time. Say the **hour followed by the number of minutes** that have gone past the hour.

Look at the hour hand. It has gone past 3.

Count around the minutes hand. 45 minutes past 3.

So the time is **3.45**

A **digital clock** shows the time in numbers. This is really easy to read. Just say the hour followed by the minutes.

- Shows the hour.

- Shows how many minutes past.

> The time is 9.30, which is 30 minutes past 9. We also say half-past nine.

Hutch's workout

What times do these show?

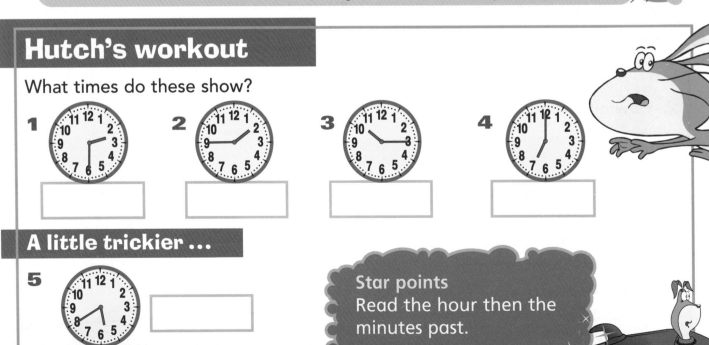

A little trickier …

5

Star points
Read the hour then the minutes past.

3-D shapes

A 3-D shape is a solid shape. Many have special names so try to learn these.

Some shapes are like boxes.

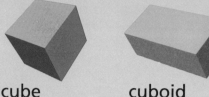

cube   cuboid

**Cubes have 6 square faces.
Cuboids have 6 rectangular
or square faces.
They both have 8 corners
and 12 edges.**

Some shapes have curves.

cylinder   sphere   cone

**Cylinders have two circles at either end.
Each circle is the same size.
A cone has a circle as a base.
A sphere is just like a ball.**

Some shapes are pyramids.

square-based
pyramid   triangle-based
pyramid

**Pyramids have triangle faces
meeting at a point.
The base shape gives its name.**

Hutch's workout

1. Name this shape.

2 Name this shape.

3 Which shape has 6 square faces?

4 How many faces does a square-based pyramid have?

A little trickier ...

5 Which shape has 6 edges, 4 corners and 4 triangle faces?

Star points Describe the faces, edges and corners.

2-D shapes

A 2-D shape is a flat shape.

Triangles have 3 straight sides

This is an equilateral triangle. It's a great word for a regular triangle with three equal sides.

Quadrilaterals have 4 straight sides

A square has 4 equal sides.

A rectangle has opposite sides equal.

Pentagons have 5 straight sides

Hexagons have 6 straight sides

Heptagons have 7 straight sides

Octagons have 8 straight sides

Hutch's workout

1 Name this shape.

2 How many sides does a heptagon have?

3 What is the name of a 5-sided shape?

4 What is the name for a regular quadrilateral?

A little trickier ...

5 What is the proper name for a triangle with 3 equal sides? (no looking!)

Star points The names describe the number of sides.

Symmetry

Some shapes are symmetrical - they have a line of symmetry.

Look at this shape.

It is symmetrical because:

- if it is folded down the middle, one half fits exactly over the other half. The fold line is the line of symmetry.

- when a mirror is placed on the line of symmetry, the half shape and its reflection show the whole shape.

These letters are symmetrical.
The line of symmetry is drawn on each.

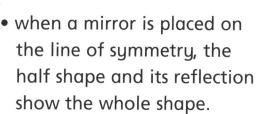

 Some shapes around us are symmetrical.

 Some shapes have no lines of symmetry:

Hutch's workout

1 Draw the line of symmetry on this shape.

2 Is this triangle symmetrical?

3 Which of these shapes is not symmetrical?

 □    □   □   □

A little trickier

4 Draw and colour spots to make a symmetrical pattern.

line of symmetry

Star points A symmetrical shape is the same on both sides.

Try to learn the points of the compass.

To remember the order, look at the initials NESW. A well-known saying to learn this order is Naughty Elephants Squirt Water!

Clockwise and **anticlockwise** are instructions for moving in different directions.

clockwise   anticlockwise

Quarter turns, half turns and **whole turns** describe how far to turn.

 A quarter turn clockwise.

 A half turn anticlockwise.

A whole turn is a complete circle. This is a whole turn clockwise.

This is a **right angle** or a 'square angle'.

Look around you and you can see lots of right angles.

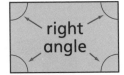

right angle   right angle

Squares and rectangles have four right angles.

Hutch's workout

1 What is the missing compass direction?

2 How many right angles has a square got?

3 Where will the arrow move to if it turns a quarter turn anti-clockwise?

A little trickier …

4 Put a dot on each of the right angles.

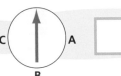 

Star points A quarter turn is a right angle.

1 Write the missing numbers.

18   16   [ ]   [ ]   10   [ ]   6

2 How much money is in the purse?

[ ]

3a Draw a line from each shape to its name.

[ ]   [ ]   [ ]   [ ]

Hexagon   Triangle   Pentagon   Rectangle

3b Tick the shapes that have a right angle.

4 A postcard costs 45p.

Sam buys two of these postcards.
How much change does he get from £1?

Show your working.

[ ]

5 Join the pairs of numbers that total 30.

15   21   18   20

10   12   9   15

6 Write these numbers in order.

41 19 27 44 14 29   [ ] [ ] [ ] [ ] [ ] [ ]

7 Use two of these number cards to make 19.

| 46 | 38 | 68 | 39 | 57 |

☐ − ☐ = 19

Show your working.

8 This graph shows the number of cans collected by five classes

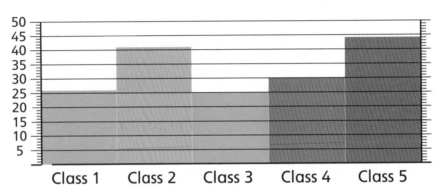

How many cans were collected altogether by Class 5 and Class 1?

☐

Show your working.

9 Write the missing number. _____ ÷ 10 = 5

☐

10 A pet shop had 16 rabbits. If $\frac{1}{4}$ of them were sold, how many rabbits are left?

Show your working.

☐

11a A film started at 7.15.

Show the time on this clock face.

11b The film is on for 1 hour 30 minutes.

At what time did it finish

12 Write these numbers in the correct place on this Venn diagram

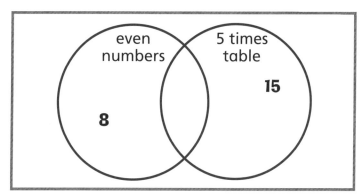

13 Use a ruler to measure the longest line.

14 Two numbers have a difference of 35. The larger number is 80.

What is the other number?

Show your working

In the home

Washing – ask your child to match the socks into pairs. Now count in twos, how many socks altogether? Remind your child that the numbers used are even numbers. Have you got an odd sock? Can they count in twos up to 25 in odd numbers, starting at 1?

- What is the next odd number after 32 … before 47?
- Is this number odd or even? 89, 38, 243, 500,

Kitchen cupboards – take a selection of tins, packets and boxes from the cupboards. Looking at the weights given on the packets ask your child to put them in weight order. Remind them to compare the hundreds digits first, then the tens, then the ones. Which pack is nearest to 500 g? 100 g? 350 g? Is the largest always the heaviest?

Bath time – give your child a clean measuring jug, ask them to fill it to 100 ml, 500 ml, 150 ml or 425 ml. Have other clean plastic containers. How much do they think each will hold? Fill the container then pour it into the jug. How much did it hold? How close was their estimate?

Cooking uses many maths skills, weighing, time, ordering and fractions. Find and follow a recipe for a cake. Let your child weigh the ingredients in grams.

- Talk about the order of the tasks. What would happen if you changed the order and cooked before mixing together the ingredients?
- Look at the time, if the cooking time is 20 minutes, when will it be ready?
- Once the cake is baked, cut the cake into half, then quarters. If you take away $\frac{1}{2}$ how many quarters did you take? If you take $\frac{1}{4}$ what is left?

In the car

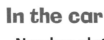

Number plates – say aloud each three digit number. Have a piece of paper with two boxes labelled 'Odd' and 'Even'. Keep a tally of how many odd and even number plates you see on your journey. Remind your child to look at the last digit.

Car park – tell your child the time. If we stay for 2 hours, what time must we return? What if we stayed for 30 minutes? 4 hours? How much will 2 hours cost? What coins could I use?

Can you make the same amount using different coins? Are there coins that cannot be used in this machine? If the machine gives change, how much change would I get from £2?

Road signs – say the shapes of signs that you pass, triangle, rectangle, square, circle …
Ask how they knew the shape 3 sides, 4 corners …?
Look for a specific shape. 'Today let's count circles.' This could include any circles, traffic lights, wheels, etc.

In the shops

Shopping questions – how much to buy? If there are 4 people in your family and they each eat two pieces of fruit a day, how many pieces of fruit do you need to buy for the week? How many yoghurts? How many eggs?

How long will it last? – Look at the 'use by' dates. If it says use by the 21st and today is the 15th, how many days can we keep it?

Shop-shapes – Look for 3-D shapes. Can you spot:

- cylinders (toilet roll, cans, biscuits)
- spheres (fruit and vegetables, oranges, onions)
- cuboids (cereal boxes, cartons)
- cubes (some tissue boxes).

Why are most card packets are cuboids?
Why are tins and jars cylinders?

Rainy days

Play Bob the Builder – give your child a tape measure to measure things around the home, ask them to estimate first, then measure each item:

- height of a cupboard
- length of a bed
- the width of the door – estimate and measure the items in a room that will fit through the door.
- the width and height of the letter box – measure the letters to see which ones fit.

Spot the right angles – set a timer for 1 minute, how many right angles can you find? Explain that rounded edges are not right angles. They could find right angles on … doors, boxes, TVs, washing machines, tiles, cupboards, picture frames, corners of rooms, etc.

Play the same game, but look for shapes – circles, triangles, squares, rectangles.

Coin count – tip out the coins in your pockets/purse.

- Sort the coins by placing them in a line starting with the highest value.
- What is the total? Start counting with the largest value coins.
- Can they make exactly 20p?
- How many different ways can they make 6p?
- If there was 27p in your pocket/purse ask how much would be needed to make 30p? 50p?

This can be repeated on different days as there will be different coins in your pockets/purse.

Answers

Counting numbers (page 2)

1   94

2   79

3   50   52

4   62   61

5   119   120   121

Counting objects (page 3)

1a   18   **1b**   34

2   Check your child has drawn 9 more.

Counting patterns (page 4)

1   25   40   45

2   6   14   16

3   30   40   80

4   18   14   8

Number sequences (page 5)

1   21   23   25

2   22   17   12

3   16   19   22

4   34   30   26

Odd and even numbers (page 6)

1a   29   31   33   **1b**   70   72   74

2   85   93   41   67

3   316   318   320

Place value (page 7)

1   30

2   600

3   50 + 7

4   79

5   145

6   500

Reading and writing numbers (page 8)

1a   94

1b   87

1c   151

2a   sixty-three

2b   seventy-five

2c   two hundred and forty-two

3   five hundred and nine

Comparing (page 9)

1   84

2   59

3   321

4   178

5   87 (smallest), 210 (biggest)

Ordering (page 10)

1   85, 81, 78, 59, 56, 37

2   8p, 13p, 18p, 60p, 65p, 82p

3   Check your child has drawn sensible answers.

4   129, 124, 115, 101, 99, 94

Estimating (page 11)

1   Check your child's answer is near to 26.

2   Check your child's answer is near to 35.

3   15, 22, 28

Rounding (page 12)

1a   40

1b   70

1c   90

1d   60

2   130

Fractions (page 13)

1   Check your child has coloured one triangle only.

2    $\dfrac{1}{4}$

3   Check your child has circled 3 zoids

4   7

5   12

Totals to 20 (page 14)

1a   11   **1b**   12

1c   14   **1d**   9

1e   11

2   5   4   3   5

Using doubles (page 15)

1a   16   **1b**   17

2a   20   **2b**   21

3   11

4   15

5   139

Adding (page 16)

1   86

2   81

3   91p

4   96

5   167

Taking away (page 17)

1   8

2   12

3   27

4   47

5    $84 - 8 = 76$

Trios (page 18)

1   3

2   6

3   6

4   12

5    $8 + 7 = 15$ $7 + 8 = 15$
       $15 - 7 = 8$ $15 - 8 = 7$

Differences (page 19)

1   7

2   7

3   6

4   23

5   24 and 32

Multiplying (page 20)

1   15

2   60

3   24

4   16

5    $3 \times 6 = 18$ or $6 \times 3 = 18$

Dividing (page 21)

1   6

2   10

3   3

4   5

5   3

2 and 3 times tables (page 22)

1   a 12   c 10   e 6   g 8   i 9
     b 4   d 30   f 15   h 20   j 3

2   a 18   c 16   e 14   g 24
     b 27   d 21   f 12   h 18

Answers

5 and 10 times tables (page 23)

1   **a** 15   **c** 10   **e** 25   **g** 40   **i** 30
    b 10   **d** 100 **f** 50   **h** 20   **j** 20

2   **a** 30   **c** 80   **e** 35   **g** 40
    b 90   **d** 70   **f** 60   **h** 45

Solving problems (page 24)

1   22
2   85m
3   120
4   13
5   9

Money (page 25)

1   83p
2   £1.60
3   245p
4   20p, 10p, 5p, 1p,
5   £6

Giving change (page 26)

1   21p
2   22p
3   42p
4   55p
5   £1.94

Sorting diagrams (page 27)

1   James and Ajit
2   Ali
3   Vicky and Sam
4   Ben and Halin
5

	dog	no dog
cat	Ali	James Ajit
no cat	Sam Vicky	Ben Halin

Pictograms (page 28)

1   25
2   Roy's Rocket
3   10
4   Sun Traveller
5   22

Bar charts (page 29)

1   Eating
2   12
3   Snoozing
4   7

Length (page 30)

1   4 cm
2   150 cm
3   80 cm
4   Check your child's answer.
5   Check your child's answer.

Answers

Mass (page 31)

1 220 g

2 2500 g

3 20 g

4 20 kg

5 Check your child's answer.

Capacity (page 32)

1 230 ml

2 1200 ml

3 6

4 Check answer using cups.

Days and months (page 33)

1 Wednesday

2 24

3 November

4 31

5 Check your child's answer.

Reading the time (page 34)

1 2.30

2 1.45

3 10.15

4 7.00

5 5.40

3-D shapes (page 35)

1 cuboid

2 cylinder

3 cube

4 5

5 triangular based pyramid or tetrahedron

2-D shapes (page 36)

1 hexagon

2 7

3 pentagon

4 square

5 equilateral

Symmetry (page 37)

1

--------------------------------->

2 yes

3 the key

4

line of symmetry

Movements and angles (page 38)

1 west

2 4

3

4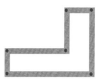

1	14, 12, 8
2	83 p
3	triangle ✓ rectangle ✓ hexagon ✗ pentagon ✗
4	2 × 45 p = 90 p £1 = 100 p 100 p − 90 p = 10 p He gets 10 p change.
5	15 → 15 10 → 20 21 → 9 12 → 18
6	14, 19, 27, 29, 41, 44
7	57 − 38 = 19
8	70
9	50
10	12

11a

11b 8.45

12

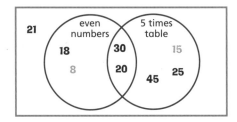

13 9 cm

14 45